2019
The Get Up and Go Diary for Busy Women

ISBN 97

Published in Ireland by
GET UP AND GO PUBLICATIONS LTD
Camboline, Hazelwood, Sligo, F91 NP04, Ireland.
Email: info@getupandgodiary.com
www.getupandgodiary.com

Compiled by Eileen Forrestal
Graphic design by Nuala Redmond
Illustrations: Sophia Murray; dreamstime.com; shutterstock.com
Printed in Ireland by GPS Colour Graphics.

2019 BANK AND PUBLIC HOLIDAYS

REPUBLIC OF IRELAND
New Year's Day, 1 January;
St Patrick's Day Bank Holiday, 18 March;
Good Friday, 19 April;
Easter Monday, 22 April;
May Day Bank Holiday, 6 May;
June Bank Holiday, 3 June;
August Bank Holiday, 5 August;
October Bank Holiday, 28 October;
Christmas Day, 25 December;
St Stephen's Day, 26 December.

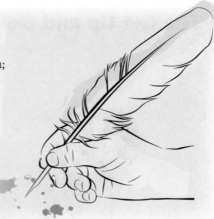

NORTHERN IRELAND
New Year's Day, 1 January;
Good Friday, 19 April;
May Day Holiday, 6 May;
Orangemen's Holiday, 12 July;
Christmas Day, 25 December;

St Patrick's Day, 18 March;
Easter Monday, 22 April;
Spring Bank Holiday, 27 May;
Summer Bank Holiday, 26 August;
Boxing Day, 26 December.

ENGLAND, SCOTLAND AND WALES
New Year's Day, 1 January;
Easter Monday, 22 April;
Spring Bank Holiday, 27 May;
Christmas Day, 25 December;

Good Friday, 19 April;
May Day Holiday, 6 May;
Summer Bank Holiday, 26 August;
Boxing Day, 26 December.

UNITED STATES OF AMERICA
New Year's Day, 1 January;
Presidents' Day, 18 February;
Independence Day, 4 July;
Columbus Day, 14 October;
Thanksgiving Day, 28 November;

Martin Luther King Day, 21 January;
Memorial Day, 27 May;
Labour Day, 2 September;
Veterans Day, 11 November;
Christmas Day, 25 December.

CANADA
New Year's Day, 1 January;
Heritage Day, 18 February;
St Patrick's Day, 18 March;
Easter Monday, 22 April;
Canada Day, 1 July;
Thanksgiving Day, 14 October;
Christmas Day, 25 December;

Family Day, 18 February;
Commonwealth Day, 11 March;
Good Friday, 19 April;
Victoria Day 20 May;
Labour Day, 2 September;
Rememberance Day, 11 November;
Boxing Day, 26 December.

AUSTRALIA (NATIONAL HOLIDAYS)
New Year's Day, 1 January;
Good Friday, 19 April;
Anzac Day 25 April;
Christmas Day, 25 December;

Australia Day, 28 January;
Easter Monday, 22 April;
Queen's Birthday, 30 September;
Boxing Day, 26 December.

2019 CALENDAR

JANAURY

Mo	Tu	We	Th	Fr	Sa	Su
	1	2	3	4	5	6
7	8	9	10	11	12	13
14	15	16	17	18	19	20
21	22	23	24	25	26	27
28	29	30	31			

FEBRUARY

Mo	Tu	We	Th	Fr	Sa	Su
				1	2	3
4	5	6	7	8	9	10
11	12	13	14	15	16	17
18	19	20	21	22	23	24
25	26	27	28			

MARCH

Mo	Tu	We	Th	Fr	Sa	Su
				1	2	3
4	5	6	7	8	9	10
11	12	13	14	15	16	17
18	19	20	21	22	23	24
25	26	27	28	29	30	31

APRIL

Mo	Tu	We	Th	Fr	Sa	Su
1	2	3	4	5	6	7
8	9	10	11	12	13	14
15	16	17	18	19	20	21
22	23	24	25	26	27	28
29	30					

MAY

Mo	Tu	We	Th	Fr	Sa	Su
		1	2	3	4	5
6	7	8	9	10	11	12
13	14	15	16	17	18	19
20	21	22	23	24	25	26
27	28	29	30	31		

JUNE

Mo	Tu	We	Th	Fr	Sa	Su
					1	2
3	4	5	6	7	8	9
10	11	12	13	14	15	16
17	18	19	20	21	22	23
24	25	26	27	28	29	30

JULY

Mo	Tu	We	Th	Fr	Sa	Su
1	2	3	4	5	6	7
8	9	10	11	12	13	14
15	16	17	18	19	20	21
22	23	24	25	26	27	28
29	30	31				

AUGUST

Mo	Tu	We	Th	Fr	Sa	Su
			1	2	3	4
5	6	7	8	9	10	11
12	13	14	15	16	17	18
19	20	21	22	23	24	25
26	27	28	29	30	31	

SEPTEMBER

Mo	Tu	We	Th	Fr	Sa	Su
						1
2	3	4	5	6	7	8
9	10	11	12	13	14	15
16	17	18	19	20	21	22
23	24	25	26	27	28	29
30						

OCTOBER

Mo	Tu	We	Th	Fr	Sa	Su
	1	2	3	4	5	6
7	8	9	10	11	12	13
14	15	16	17	18	19	20
21	22	23	24	25	26	27
28	29	30	31			

NOVEMBER

Mo	Tu	We	Th	Fr	Sa	Su
				1	2	3
4	5	6	7	8	9	10
11	12	13	14	15	16	17
18	19	20	21	22	23	24
25	26	27	28	29	30	

DECEMBER

Mo	Tu	We	Th	Fr	Sa	Su
						1
2	3	4	5	6	7	8
9	10	11	12	13	14	15
16	17	18	19	20	21	22
23	24	25	26	27	28	29
30	31					

Forgive the past – let it go
Live the present – the power of now
Create the future – thoughts become things

Dear Reader,

We are delighted that you're holding this Get Up and Go diary in your hands today. You are about to embark on a wonderful journey with 'the world's best loved transformational diary'.

Whether you have chosen this diary for yourself or received it as gift, we know it will fill you with inspiration, encouragement, motivation and empowerment as you progress towards fulfilling your goals and dreams in the coming year.

You might like to share some of your goals and experiences with our ever growing Get Up and Go community too. You can do that easily at **www.getupandgodiary.com**. When you're there you'll be able to follow our blog, be informed of new products, get access to upcoming events and see details of special offers too – it will be worth your while.

You may also like to follow us on Facebook, Twitter and Instagram for additional timely words of inspiration and encouragement.

Whether this is your first Get Up and Go diary or you're a regular and loyal customer, we thank you, and we trust that you will benefit from the carefully chosen words contained herein. If you enjoy your diary we would love it if you would share it with your family and friends.

Oh, there's something extra we think you'll love too. This year there's a beautiful and special surprise built in to every Get Up and Go Diary. Through our partnership with the Global Giving Initiative www.B1G1.com this diary is changing lots of lives – a contribution from each diary goes towards children in rural Cambodia getting access to clean water, children in rural India enjoying e-learning where there was no school before and we're helping to build a school in Kenya. You'll see more about all of that at www.getupandgodiary.com too.

And it all happens because people like you love their Get Up and Go diary. Thank you so much for being one of them.

With very best wishes for the year ahead,

Eileen, Brendan and the Get Up and Go team.

This diary belongs to: _____

Address: _____

Tel: _____ Email: _____

Emergency telephone number: _____

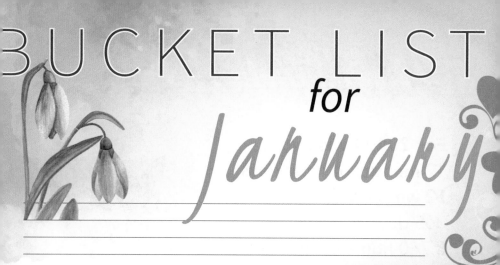

BUCKET LIST
for
January

IT IS TIME TO START THE NEW YEAR RIGHT

It is time to:
- Start planning for success.
- Visualise attainable goals.
- Design an environment that will support you moving forward.
- Drop the bad habits.
- Start the good habits.
- Commit to your better self.
- Overcome the procrastination that is holding you back.
- Establish a process, rhythm, behaviors and actions for success.

It is time to start your journey to achieve anything that you set your mind to accomplish.

January

For 2019 I wish you:
12 months of happiness;
52 weeks of fun;
365 days of success;
8,760 hours of great health; and
525,600 lucky minutes.
Happy New Year!

Courage is like a muscle. We strengthen it by use.
Ruth Gordon

The most important thing is to enjoy your life – to be happy – it's all that matters.
Audrey Hepburn

TUESDAY 1
HAPPY NEW YEAR!

Trust your intuition

MAKE THIS YOUR BEST YEAR
EVER

Keep the promises you make to yourself.
Concentrate on what matters.

Choose happiness.

Go beyond what normally stops you.
Do what you love and love what you do.
TRY SOMETHING DIFFERENT.
Break an old habit and form a new one.

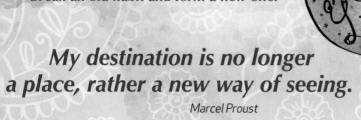

*My destination is no longer
a place, rather a new way of seeing.*

Marcel Proust

WEDNESDAY 2

Say yes to the longings of your heart

THURSDAY 3

Recognise your strengths

FRIDAY 4

Put your best foot forward

January

My great hope for us as young women is to start being kinder to ourselves so we can be kinder to each other; to stop shaming ourselves and other people for things we don't know the full story on – whether someone is too fat, too skinny, too short, too tall, too loud, too quiet, too anything. There is a sense that we are all 'too' something, and that we are not 'enough' anything.

Emma Stone

Be thankful for where you've been, okay with where you are, and excited about where you're headed.

SATURDAY **5**

Let go of expectations

SUNDAY **6**

Focus on excellence

I PROMISE MYSELF

To be so strong that nothing
can disturb my peace of mind.
To talk health, happiness, and prosperity
to every person I meet.
To make all my friends feel that there
is something worthwhile in them.
To look at the sunny side of everything
and make my optimism come true.
To think only the best, to work only for the best,
and to expect only the best.
To be just as enthusiastic about the success of others
as I am about my own.
To forget the mistakes of the past
and press on to the greater achievements of the future.
To wear a cheerful expression at all times
and give a smile to every living creature I meet.
To give so much time to the improvement of myself
that I have no time to criticise others.
To be too large for worry, too noble for anger, too strong for fear,
and too happy to permit the presence of trouble.
To think well of myrself and to proclaim this fact to the world,
not in loud words but great deeds.
To live in faith that the whole world is on my side
so long as I am true to the best that is in me.

Christian D Larson

Sometimes,
this is my busy –
and I will not
apologise
for it.

Brittin Oakman

MONDAY 7

Put your passion into action

TUESDAY 8

Decide what is important to you

You start dying slowly
if you do not travel,
if you do not read,
if you do not listen to the sounds of life,
if you do not appreciate yourself.

You start dying slowly when you kill your self-esteem,
when you do not let others help you.
You start dying slowly if you become a slave to your
habits, walking everyday on the same paths,
if you do not change your routine,
if you do not wear different colours or you do not
speak to those you don't know.

You start dying slowly if you avoid passion and
its turbulent emotions, those that make your eyes
glisten and your heart beat fast.
You start dying slowly if you do not change your
life when you are not satisfied with your job, or
with your love, or with your surroundings.
If you do not risk what is safe for the uncertain,
if you do not go after a dream,
if you do not allow yourself,
at least once in your lifetime,
to run away from sensible advice.

Pablo Neruda

Stop wearing your wishbone where your backbone ought to be.

Elizabeth Gilbert

WEDNESDAY 9

Acknowledge your achievements

THURSDAY 10

Be generous to yourself first

FRIDAY 11

Face the future with courage and confidence

SATURDAY 12

Explore the limits of your comfort zone

SUNDAY 13

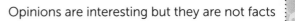

Opinions are interesting but they are not facts

January

Positive thinking will let you do everything better than negative thinking will.

Zig Ziglar

MONDAY **14**

Feel the fear and do it anyway

TUESDAY **15**

Stretch the edges of your thinking

Attitude is a choice. Happiness is a choice. Optimism is a choice. Kindness is a choice. Giving is a choice. Respect is a choice. Whatever choices you make makes you. Choose wisely.

Roy T Bennett

WEDNESDAY **16**

Choose your friends carefully

> **One of the most tragic things I know about human nature is that all of us tend to put off living. We are all dreaming of some magical rose garden over the horizon instead of enjoying the roses that are blooming outside our windows today.**
>
> *Dale Carnegie*

THURSDAY 17

You are responsible for your own journey

FRIDAY 18

Sort out your priorities

SATURDAY 19

Get rid of excuses

SUNDAY 20

Look for the solution in every challenge

January

Sadness gives depth. Happiness gives height. Sadness gives roots. Happiness gives branches. Happiness is like a tree going into the sky, and sadness is like the roots going down into the womb of the earth. Both are needed, and the higher a tree goes, the deeper it goes, simultaneously. The bigger the tree, the bigger will be its roots. In fact, it is always in proportion. That's its balance.

Osho

You're only given a little spark of madness. You mustn't lose it,

Robin Williams

Choc chip slice

FROM MAMA RAE

INGREDIENTS
1 can chickpeas
½ cup almond butter
⅓ cup maple syrup
1 teaspoon vanilla
¼ teaspoon baking powder
¼ teaspoon baking soda
¼ teaspoon salt
½ cup choc chips

THE HOW-TO PART
Drain and rinse the chickpeas, process in food processor with almond butter, maple syrup, vanilla, baking powder, baking soda and salt. Add ¼ cup choc chips and stir in. Pour into slice tin and smooth. Sprinkle ¼ cup choc chips on the top and press down. Bake for 30-35 minutes at 175 degrees

MAMA RAE'S INSIDE SECRETS
You can use any of the nut butters, it doesn't affect the taste. Substitute your favourite sweetener for the maple syrup.

MONDAY **21**

What would someone you admire do in this situation?

TUESDAY **22**

Don't look back, you're not going that way

With mirth and laughter let old wrinkles come.

William Shakespeare

WEDNESDAY 23

Criticism gets you nowhere

THURSDAY 24

When principle is involved, stand your ground

FRIDAY 25

Avoid making assumptions

SATURDAY 26

It pays to listen

SUNDAY 27

Encourage others

MONDAY **28**

Begin the day with gratitude

TUESDAY **29**

Two heads are better than one

WEDNESDAY **30**

Empower your dreams in the pursuit of them

THURSDAY **31**

Spend time with enthusiastic people

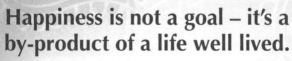

Happiness is not a goal – it's a by-product of a life well lived.

Eleanor Roosevelt

It was only a sunny smile,
and little it cost in the giving,
but like morning light,
it scattered the night,
and made the day worth living.
F Scott Fitzgerald

BUCKET LIST for February

A very wise man once said: "I don't know, go ask a woman".

LOVE in the air

February

It's been my experience that you can nearly always enjoy things if you make up your mind firmly that you will.

Anne of Green Gables

FRIDAY 1

Your vision is in your minds eye

Do more than belong; participate
Do more than care; help
Do more than believe; practice
Do more than be fair; be kind
Do more than forgive; forget.
Do more than dream; work.

William Arthur Ward

Ninety-nine percent of who you are is invisible and untouchable.

Buckminster Fuller

You are in charge of your own happiness; you don't need to wait for other people's permission to be happy.

T Bennett

> **Beautiful young people are accidents of nature, but beautiful old people are works of art.**
>
> *Eleanor Roosevelt*

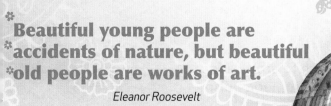

Strawberry cake

INGREDIENTS
175g butter, softened
175g golden caster sugar
2 medium eggs
175g ground almonds
175g self-raising flour
1tsp ground cinnamon
500g strawberries, hulled and halved
Icing sugar, for dusting
You will also need:
23cm (9in) loose-based cake tin, buttered and lined

THE HOW-TO PART
Set the oven to 180°C/350°F/Gas Mark 4 and line the 23cm cake tin with greaseproof paper. Beat the butter and sugar until light and fluffy. Beat in the eggs and 2tbsps warm water. Mix in nuts, flour and spice. Spread half the mixture in the tin to the edges. Place most of the strawberries on top (reserve a few small halves), then spread the rest of the cake mixture on top and scatter with the rest of the fruit. Bake for about 1 hour 10 minutes. Check after an hour, and if it's getting too brown, cover with paper. Cool in the tin for 10 minutes, then loosen edges with a knife. Slide cake onto a plate and dust with icing sugar. Serve warm or cooled, with cream or yogurt.

SATURDAY **2**

Acknowledge your accomplishments each day

SUNDAY **3**

Love the home you live in

Letting go

To let go does not mean to stop caring,
it means I can't do it for someone else.
To let go is not to cut myself off,
it's the realisation I can't control another.
To let go is not to enable,
but to allow learning from natural consequences.
To let go is to admit powerlessness,
which means the outcome is not in my hands.
To let go is not to try to change or blame another,
it's to make the most of myself.
To let go is not to care for, but to care about.
To let go is not to fix, but to be supportive.
To let go is not to judge,
but to allow another to be a human being.
To let go is not to be in the middle arranging all the outcomes,
but to allow others to affect their destinies.
To let go is not to be protective,
it's to permit another to face reality.
To let go is not to deny, but to accept.
To let go is not to nag, scold or argue, but instead
to search out my own shortcomings and correct them.
To let go is not to adjust everything to my desires,
but to take each day as it comes and cherish myself in it.
To let go is not to criticise or regulate anybody,
but to try to become what I dream I can be.
To let go is not to regret the past,
but to grow and live for the future.
To let go is to fear less and love more.

February

Take chances, make mistakes.
That's how you grow.
Pain nourishes your courage.
You have to fail in order
to practice being brave.

Mary Tyler Moore

Taking joy in living is a woman's best cosmetic.

Rosalind Russell

MONDAY 4

You empower your dreams in the pursuit of them

TUESDAY 5

Your wealth is hiding under the very thing you are afraid to do

---

WEDNESDAY 6

Master your emotions or they will master you

And above all, watch with glittering eyes the whole world around you because the greatest secrets are always hidden in the most unlikely places. Those who don't believe in magic will never find it.

Roald Dahl

February

THURSDAY **7**

Be aware that we each see the world from our own point of view

FRIDAY **8**

Tap into your natural passion

SATURDAY **9**

Develop the talents you naturally have

> ## We are called to be architects of the future, not its victims.
> *Buckminster Fuller*

SUNDAY **10**

Your life is your canvas, make it your masterpiece

One word frees us of all the weight and pain of life:
that word is love.
Sophocles

MONDAY **11**

Give your fears to the wind

TUESDAY **12**

Your life is a hero's journey

WEDNESDAY **13**

If you are not expanding you're shrinking

Love is just a word until someone comes along and gives it meaning.
Paulo Coelho

THURSDAY **14**
St Valentine's Day

Practice healthy thinking

You can have unbelievable intelligence, you can have
connections, you can have opportunities fall out of the sky.
But in the end, hard work is the true, enduring
characteristic of successful people.
Marsha Evans

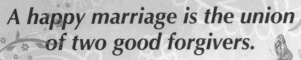

February

A happy marriage is the union of two good forgivers.

Ruth Graham

FRIDAY 15

Accept what you have not yet accepted

SATURDAY 16

Have a bigger why

SUNDAY 17

Be proud of your game

WHAT I LEARNED FROM CATS

Make the world your playground. When ever you miss the sand box, cover up the evidence. Dragging a sock over it helps.

> *Many things can cause us to worry, but a kind word or deed can do wonders. Sometimes that's all we need to feel better.*
>
> Kate Klise

MONDAY 18

The universe is unfolding exactly as it should

TUESDAY 19

Encourage the dreams of others

WEDNESDAY 20

Do what you know to do

THURSDAY 21

Complaining is unproductive

A sister is a gift to the heart, a friend to the spirit, a golden thread to the meaning of life.

Isadora James

People do not change, they are merely revealed.

Anne Enright

FRIDAY **22**

Take it one day at a time

SATURDAY **23**

Be prepared for surprises

SUNDAY **24**

Thinking doesn't change anything

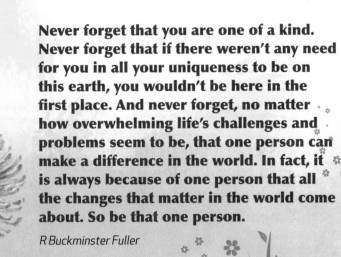

Never forget that you are one of a kind. Never forget that if there weren't any need for you in all your uniqueness to be on this earth, you wouldn't be here in the first place. And never forget, no matter how overwhelming life's challenges and problems seem to be, that one person can make a difference in the world. In fact, it is always because of one person that all the changes that matter in the world come about. So be that one person.

R Buckminster Fuller

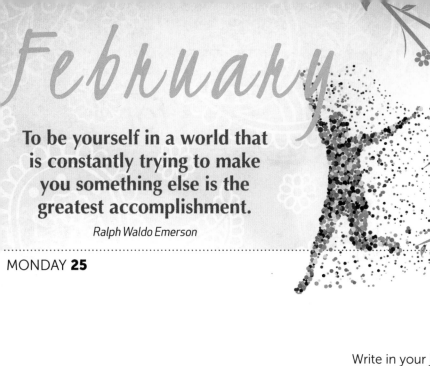

February

To be yourself in a world that
is constantly trying to make
you something else is the
greatest accomplishment.

Ralph Waldo Emerson

MONDAY **25**

Write in your journal

TUESDAY **26**

Stay open and curious

WEDNESDAY **27**

Do not be afraid to fail

THURSDAY **28**

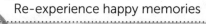

Re-experience happy memories

BUCKET LIST

for
March

*The minute you begin to do
what you really want to do, it's
really a different kind of life.*

R Buckminster Fuller

Many people think excitement is happiness.
But when you are excited you are not peaceful.
True happiness is based on peace.

Thich Nhat Hanh

The longer we dwell on our misfortunes, the greater is their power to harm us.

Voltaire

There are three constants in life — change, choice and principles.

Stephen Covey

FOLLOW YOUR HEART AND DREAM

The trick is in what one emphasises. We either make ourselves miserable, or we make ourselves happy. The amount of work is the same.

Carlos Castaneda

FRIDAY **1**

Success does not require misery

March

Time to believe in Magic

So many gods,
So many creeds,
So many paths that wind and wind,
While just the art of being kind
Is all this sad world needs.

Ella Wheeler Wilcox

Destiny is a name often given in retrospect to choices that had dramatic consequences.

JK Rowling

The bitterest tears shed over graves are for words left unsaid and deeds left undone.

Harriet Beecher Stowe

SATURDAY 2

Create a life worth loving

SUNDAY 3

Your best contribution is a good mood

Hope is a waking dream.
Aristotle

Butter chicken curry

INGREDIENTS
800g boneless, skinned chicken thighs,
cut into bite size pieces.
2 cloves garlic, peeled and crushed.
2cm ginger, peeled, finely grated.
1/2 tsp salt
1/2 tsp chilli powder
1 1/2 tbsp lemon juice
75ml natural yoghurt
1/2 tsp garam masala
1/2 tsp ground turmeric
1 tsp ground cumin
1-2 tbsp vegetable oil

SAUCE
11/2 tbsp melteed butter or ghee
2 cloves garlic, peeled, finely chopped
2cm ginger, peeled, finely chopped
2 cloves
1 cardamum pod
tsp garam masala
tsp turmuric
tsp chilli powder
250 mls tomato puree
tsp lemon juice
40gm salted butter
100mls cream
1 tbsp chopped corriander

THE HOW-TO PART
Mix chicken in a bowl with garlic, ginger, salt, chilli powder and lemon juice. Cover
with cling foil and chill for 30 minutes. Mix yoghurt, garam masala, cumin, turmeric,
and add to the chicken, to marinate. Cover and chill for 3-4 hrs. Preheat oven to 160C
GAS 4. Put marinated chicken pieces on a grill rack and bake for 12-18 min.
For the sauce: Heat the ghee or butter in a pan and add the garlic and ginger. Fry for
1-2 min, add the cardamom, cloves, coriander, garam masala, turmeric and chilli
powder. Stir well and fry for further 1-2 mins. Stir in the tomato puree and lemon juice
and cook for another 2-3 mins. Add the chicken pieces to the sauce and stir well to
coat. Finally, add the butter and cream and stir continuously until the butter has melted
and the sauce is smooth. Taste and adjust the seasoning. Transfer to a warm bowl and
serve hot, garnished with chopped coriander.

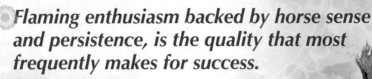

Flaming enthusiasm backed by horse sense and persistence, is the quality that most frequently makes for success.

Dale Carnegie

MONDAY **4**

Don't over-dramatise your life

It is easy to sit up and take notice. What is difficult is getting up and taking action.

Honore de Balzac

TUESDAY **5**

Let failure point you to success

WEDNESDAY **6**

90%of those who fail are not defeated ... they quit

THURSDAY **7**

Develop the talent you have

March

*I don't know what your destiny will be,
but one thing I know: the only ones among
you who will be really happy are those who
have sought and found how to serve.*

Albert Schweitzer

**What sunshine is to flowers, smiles are to humanity.
These are but trifles, to be sure; but scattered along
life's pathway, the good they do is inconceivable.**

Jospeh Addison

FRIDAY 8

Bring more fun to the workplace

SATURDAY 9

Take action to cause results

SUNDAY 10

You have everything you need

March

If you spend your whole life waiting for the storm, you'll never enjoy the sunshine.

Morris West

MONDAY 11

Pass a genuine compliment

HEY YOU

Yes, you. Stop being unhappy with yourself. You are perfect. Stop wishing you looked like someone else or wishing people liked you as much as they like someone else. Stop trying to get attention from those who hurt you. Stop hating your body, your face, your personality, your quirks. Love them. Without those things you wouldn't be you. Why would you want to be anyone else? Be confident in who you are. Smile. It will draw people in. If anyone hates on you because you are happy with yourself, then you stick your middle finger in the air and say "'Screw it! My happiness will not depend on others any more. I'm happy because I love who I am. I accept my flaws. I accept my imperfections. They make me me, and me is petty amazing. I love being me.

Life isn't about finding yourself.
Life is about creating yourself.

George Bernard Shaw

TUESDAY 12

Anything is possible in committed dialogue

There are two ways to be fooled. One is to believe what wasn't true; the other is to refuse to believe what is true.

Soren Kierkegaard

WEDNESDAY 13

Put your dreams to work for you

THURSDAY 14

Just take the next small step

FRIDAY 15

Don't argue with the laws of nature

Surround yourself with people who make you happy. People who make you laugh. Who help you when you're in need. People who genuinely care. They are the ones worth keeping in your life. Everyone else is just passing through.

Karl Marx

March

SATURDAY 16

You are worthy of your own love and compassion

12 POWERFUL QUESTIONS
TO START MY DAY:

What am I grateful for?
Who do I love?
Why am I happy?
What do I love about my life?
What is my intention for today?
How will I show up today?
What am I committed to?
What will I discover today?
What is my deepest desire today?
Where can I step up today?
Where can I make a positive difference today?
Who can I inspire or encourage today?

SUNDAY 17
Happy St. Patricks Day

Seek to understand more

There is nothing in a caterpillar that tells you it's going to be a butterfly.

Buckminster Fuller

MONDAY 18
Bank holiday

Prioritise your time

TUESDAY 19

Be discontent with the status quo

WEDNESDAY 20

Pay attention to your education – it's lifelong

THURSDAY 21

You are enough

FRIDAY 22

Short cuts make for long delays

March

*She'd passed the fear barrier, and she'd lived,
and she'd discovered not certain death,
as she'd imagined, but impossible splendor.
What other beautiful things had fear been
hiding from her? What else had the curse
long kept her from discovering?
For the first time in a long time,
she wanted to find out.*

Krystal Sutherland

**Extraordinary people survive under
the most terrible circumstances and
they become more extraordinary
because of it.**

Robertson Davies

SATURDAY 23

Develop a can-do, will-do mind-set

SUNDAY 24

The future you see is the future you get

The most powerful weapon on earth is the human soul on fire.

Ferdinand Foch

Nothing gives one person so much advantage over another as to remain cool and unruffled under all circumstances.

Thomas Jefferson

MONDAY **25**

Most of what you worry about never happens

TUESDAY **26**

Be gentle on yourself

WEDNESDAY **27**

Successful people have successful habits

THURSDAY **28**

Kick the 'but' out of your life

FRIDAY **29**

Everyone has a unique and valid point of view

SATURDAY **30**

Join an evening class

My mother was the most beautiful woman
I ever saw. All I am I owe to my mother.
I attribute all my success in life to
the moral, intellectual and
physical education I
received from her.

George Washington

*My mother handed
down respect for
possibilities – and
the will to
grasp them.*

Alice Walker

Unhappiness is often
caused by overthinking.
Guard against overthought
and underaction.
Think yourself
happy and act
yourself happy.

SUNDAY **31**
Mother's Day

Enjoy being in the driving seat of your life

for

April

Cocktail "Mai Tai"

4 cl White Rum
2 cl Dark Rum
15 cl Orange Cura
15 cl Orgeat Syrup
1 cl Fresh Lime Juice

*Only I can change
my life. No one can
do it for me.*
Carol Burnett

**There's no point in being grown up
if you can't be childish sometimes.**
Dr Who

April

*I found I had less and less to say, until finally,
I became silent, and began to listen.
I discovered in the silence, the voice of God.*

Soren Kierkegaard

MONDAY 1

Be generous

TUESDAY 2

Get to know the person in the mirror

WEDNESDAY 3

Keep the big picture In mind

THURSDAY 4

It's ok to admit you are not superwoman

FRIDAY **5**

We cannot succeed alone

SATURDAY **6**

Put your dreams to work for you

SUNDAY **7**

Value your wellbeing above all else

One day," he said, "everybody's gonna wake up and realise their parents are human beings, just like them. Sometimes they're good people, sometimes they're not.
Krystal Sutherland

People grow through experience if they meet life honestly and courageously. This is how character is built.

Eleanor Roosevelt

*Optimism is a happiness magnet.
If you stay positive, good things
and good people will be drawn to you.*

Mary Lou Retton

MONDAY **8**

Ask the universe for advice

TUESDAY **9**

Phone an old friend for a good chin-wag

WEDNESDAY **10**

Courage and confidence grow from within

THURSDAY **11**

Face your fears and take action

If you judge people, you don't have time to love them.

Mother Teresa

FRIDAY **12**

Maturity is being at peace with imperfection

SATURDAY **13**

Every problem has a solution

SUNDAY **14**

Add value wherever you are

Delicious smoothie

1 medium ripe banana, sliced.
1 cup fresh pineapple, diced.
½ cup fresh strawberries.
³/₄ cup milk.
1 Tbsp honey or agave nectar.
6 ice cubes or 1 cup crushed ice.
Whipped cream, chocolate syrup, and
a maraschino cherry for garnish.

Blend the pineapple and strawberry in a blender until
mashed. Add the other ingredients and blend on high
until smooth. Pour into two frozen parfait, coupe, or
glass of your choice. Top with a dollop of whipped
cream, a drizzle of chocolate syrup, and a maraschino
cherry.

The most important thing is not to think very much about oneself. To investigate candidly the charge, but not fussily, not very anxiously.
On no account to retaliate by going to the other extreme – thinking too much.

Virginia Woolf

April

One's life has value so long as one attributes value to the life of others, by means of love, friendship, indignation and compassion.

Simone de Beauvoir

MONDAY **15**

Feedback is the breakfast of champions

TUESDAY **16**

Accept compliments graciously and gracefully

WEDNESDAY **17**

Self expression is essential to life

THURSDAY **18**

Take what you do seriously but yourself lightly

FRIDAY **19**
Good Friday

Here today, gone tomorrow

SATURDAY **20**

Be aware of the competition but don't compete with it

This is my wish for you:
Comfort on difficult days,
Smiles when sadness intrudes,
Laughter to kiss your lips,
Sunsets to warm your heart,
Gentle hugs when spirits sag,
Friendships to brighten your day,
Beauty for your eyes to see,
Confidence for when you doubt,
Faith so you can believe,
Courage to know yourself,
Patience to accept the truth,
Love to complete your life.

I was busy taking deeper breaths.
I was busy silencing irrational thoughts.
I was busy calming a racing heart.
I was busy telling myself I am okay.

SUNDAY **21**
Easter Sunday

Connect with your tribe

April

We gain strength, courage and confidence by each experience in which we really stop to look fear in the face. We must do that which we think we cannot.

Eleanor Roosevelt

All our dreams can come true if we have the courage to pursue them.

Walt Disney

Getting over painful experience is much like crossing monkey bars – you have to let go in order to move forward.

CS Lewis

MONDAY 22
Easter Monday

Have a personal mission statement for your life

TUESDAY 23

Let some things wait until tomorrow

WEDNESDAY 24

All will be well

I release myself from all guilt.
I forgive myself for judging me guilty.
Jonathan Lockwood Huie

I feel a resurgence of my six-year-old self... that little warrior goddess of a girl reminding me of who I was when I was little, before the world got its hands on me.

Jennifer Elisabeth

THURSDAY **25**

Be a clearing for miracles

FRIDAY **26**

Start now; the time will never be just right

SATURDAY **27**

What gets measured gets managed

SUNDAY **28**

A trade not properly learnt is an enemy

You are not what you think you are, but what you think... you are

You are the master of your fate

THINGS MY MOTHER TAUGHT ME

My mother taught me to appreciate a job well done: *"If you're going to kill each other do it outside, I've just finished cleaning the floor."*

My mother taught me religion: *"You better pray that will come out of the carpet."*

My mother taught me about time travel: *"If you don't straighten up I'm going to knock you into the middle of next week."*

My mother taught me reason: *"Because I said so, that's why."*

My mother taught me logic: *"If you fall out of that swing and break your neck, don't come running to me."*

My mother taught me foresight: *"Make sure you wear clean underwear, in case you're in an accident."*

My mother taught me irony: *"Keep crying and I'll give you something to cry about about."*

My mother taught me about osmosis: *"Shut your mouth and eat your breakfast."*

My mother taught me about contortionism: *"Will you look at the dirt on the back of your neck."*

My mother taught me about stamina: *"You'll sit there until all that dinner is finished."*

BUCKET LIST
for
May

There's nothing better than a good friend, except for a good friend with chocolate.

_____
_____
_____
_____
_____
_____
_____
_____
_____
_____
_____
_____

Everyone may not be good, but there's always something good in everyone. Never judge anyone shortly because every saint has a past and every sinner has a future.

Oscar Wilde

WEDNESDAY **1**

Don't let regrets replace your dreams

Tomato, basil and courgette mini pizzas

FOR THE PIZZA DOUGH
250g self-raising flour/plain flour and three tsp baking powder
4tbsp olive oil
100ml warm water

FOR THE TOMATO SAUCE
1 tin chopped tomatoes
1 onion
2tbsp olive oil
2 cloves garlic
1 tin chopped tomatoes
1tbsp tomato puree
1tbsp dried oregano or mixed herbs

FOR THE TOPPINGS
A few handfuls of multi-coloured tomatoes
Small handful of fresh basil
A large mozzarella ball
A courgette
The tomato sauce can also be used on pasta, as a base for
a bolognese, or wherever a tomato sauce is called for!

THE HOW-TO PART
Preheat oven to 230°C/210°C fan/Gas Mark 8. Lightly grease and line two large baking trays.
Mix flour in a bowl. Pour in the oil and most of the water, and mix together to form a dough. Knead
on a lightly floured surface, turning, folding and pressing until the dough is even and smooth (at least
5-10 minutes). Cut the dough with a sharp knife to create eight even balls. Roll each ball out on a
lightly floured work surface into mini round pizza bases, approx. 5mm thick, and transfer to baking
sheet. To make the tomato sauce, finely chop the onion and sauté with the oil in a frying pan over a
low heat until soft, then crush the garlic and add to the pan for another couple of minutes Add the
tin of tomatoes, tomato puree and herbs and continue to sauté for another 10 minutes. Spread a
generous layer of tomato sauce over each pizza base, then add sliced tomatoes, basil, mozzarella
and some thin courgette slices. Bake in the oven for about 10-15 minutes, until the crusts are
golden and the topping bubbling.

THURSDAY **2**

Don't worry; be happy

Recover the innocent eye of childhood that brings wonder and magic to everyday life.

FRIDAY **3**

If you want to be loved, be loving

SATURDAY **4**

Your attitude determines your altitude

SUNDAY **5**

Perhaps what you are looking for is right here

Women must try to do things as men have tried. When they fail, their failure must be but a challenge to others

Amelia Earhart

Never underestimate the power you have to take your life in a new direction.

Germany Kent

TIPS TO FINANCIAL FREEDOM

MASTER YOUR MONEY MINDSET: Take responsibility for your financial situation and learn how to transform bad 'spending' habits into good 'investing' habits.

BUDGET EFFECTIVELY: Learn exactly where your money is going each month and how to create and manage your own budget.

FIND YOUR TRUE PASSION: Identify your true purpose, discover your unique drive and use your energy to generate your income doing what you love.

STAY MOTIVATED: Learn how to stay motivated, or allow someone to motivate you when you don't feel like it, to overcome any obstacles that challenge you.

TAKE OWNERSHIP OF YOUR CAREER: Climb your own success ladder, become an entrepreneur, and learn how by providing great value will make you a good living. Owners Earn.

The most difficult thing is the decision to act, the rest is merely tenacity. The fears are paper tigers. You can do anything you decide to do. You can act to change and control your life; and the procedure, the process is its own reward.

Amelia Earhart

MONDAY **6**
Bank holiday

Get into the driving seat of your life

May

The more one does and sees and feels, the more one is able to do, and the more genuine may be one's appreciation of fundamental things like home, and love, and understanding companionship.

TUESDAY 7

You have excuses or you have results

WEDNESDAY 8

Set aside time to enjoy your own company

THURSDAY 9

Live up to your own standards and ideals

FRIDAY 10

Be willing to care and care to be willing

May

I believe that a girl should not do what she thinks she should do, but should find out through experience what she wants to do. No borders, just horizons – only freedom. Everyone has oceans to fly, if they have the heart to do it. Is it reckless? Maybe. But what do dreams know of boundaries?

Amelia Earhart

SATURDAY 11

Expect miracles to get miracles

SUNDAY 12

Give more than is expected of you

Hope is the thing with feathers that perches in the soul – and sings the tunes without the words – and never stops at all.

Emily Dickinson

Dogs are better than human beings because they know but do not tell.

Emily Dickinson

TIPS TO STAY
COOL

Breathe before you act. Taking a slow deep breath before engaging in verbal 'war fare' will help calm the mind and ease the situation.

If someone offends you, address it politely. Don't hold it in or act it out. Simply say it is not acceptable and request an apology. Know what triggers you and learn a new response. Be inventive. **You know what triggers you**, others sometimes don't!

The old counting-to-ten trick works. If you've never tried it, I suggest you give it a shot. By getting upset you are only escalating the drama.

Be above it all. Keep it all in perspective. Remember you have a great life and minor inconveniences are just a part of the real world that we all have to live in.

Don't sweat the small stuff. Birth, illness and death are the real biggies in life. Learning to let go the small things will help you to live longer and happier.

Take a few more deep breaths. Forcing fresh air into your lungs sends oxygen to your heart and brain and acts as a calming agent. Breathe slowly.

Check in with your heart. Asking yourself if this is truly worth getting steamed up over? Is this who you want to be, and how you want to act?

Think before you speak. Words have impact … and consequences. Saying to yourself what you might say to another, and imagining how he or she will take it, is a great way to prevent downward spirals from occurring.

Ask yourself, "Am I in control of this situation?" The answer is 'Yes'! If you lose your cool – you lose the battle! **Stay calm, stay cool, stay in control.**

May

At times our own light goes out and is rekindled by a spark from another person. Each of us has cause to think with deep gratitude of those who have lighted the flame within us.

Albert Schweitzer

MONDAY **13**

Have dinner by candle light

TUESDAY **14**

Be willing to accept the advice you give to others

WEDNESDAY **15**

Stay connected with your support network

THURSDAY **16**

Don't be the one holding you back

Do not stand at my grave and weep.
I am not there. I do not sleep.
I am a thousand winds that blow.
I am the diamond glints on snow.
I am the sunlight on ripened grain.
I am the gentle autumn rain.
When you awaken in the morning's hush.
I am the swift uplifting rush
Of quiet birds in circled flight.
I am the soft stars that shine at night.
Do not stand at my grave and cry;
I am not there. I did not die.

Mary Elizabeth Frye

FRIDAY **17**

It takes time to build strong relationships

SATURDAY **18**

Be empowered by empowering others

SUNDAY **19**

People just do what they do

A good friend is like a bra: hard to find one you're comfortable with, always provides support, holds you tight and is always close to your heart.

May

Even if you have a problem, you don't need to be one.

Helen Keller

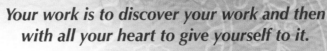

Your work is to discover your work and then with all your heart to give yourself to it.

Buddha

MONDAY 20

Small talk may cause big disaster

TUESDAY 21

Notice what stops you – and go beyond

WEDNESDAY 22

Desire is the starting point of all achievement

> *Balance is not something you find, it's something you create.*

THURSDAY 23

Life is short – choose to be happy

FRIDAY 24

Differentiate your desires from your hopes and wishes

SATURDAY 25

There is no such thing as something for nothing

SUNDAY 26

Do not underestimate the dreamer

If you carry joy in your heart, you can heal any moment.

Carlos Santana

MONDAY **27**

Go for a long walk and enjoy the scenery on the way

TUESDAY **28**

Be comfortable with growing older

WEDNESDAY **29**

Every failure brings with it the seed of an equivalent success

THURSDAY **30**

Don't indulge in needless suffering

FRIDAY **31**

Make new friends

You cannot do a kindness too soon, for you never know how soon it will be too late.

Ralph Waldo Emerson

_____

_____

_____

_____

_____

_____

_____

_____

_____

I'M GONNA BE A BEAR

In this life I'm a woman,
In my next life I would like to come back as a bear.
When you're a bear, you get to hibernate; you do nothing but
sleep for six months. I could deal with that. Before you hibernate,
you're supposed to eat yourself silly. I could deal with that. When you're
a mama bear, you birth your children, who are the size of walnuts,
while you are sleeping, and wake up to partially grown cute, cuddly
cubs. I could deal with that too.
When you're a Momma bear, everyone knows you mean business.
You swat anyone who bothers your cubs. If your cubs get out of line,
you swat them too. I could deal with that.
If you're a bear, your mate expects you to wake up growling,
to have hairy legs and excess body fat.
Yup! I'm gonna be a bear.

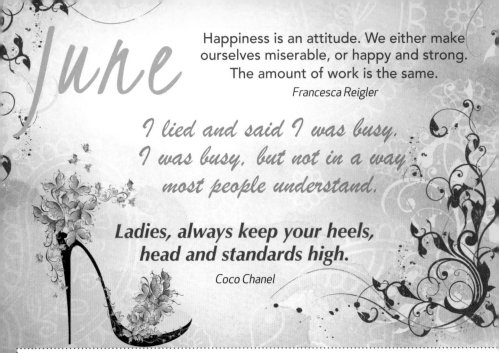

June

Happiness is an attitude. We either make ourselves miserable, or happy and strong. The amount of work is the same.

Francesca Reigler

I lied and said I was busy. I was busy, but not in a way most people understand.

Ladies, always keep your heels, head and standards high.

Coco Chanel

SATURDAY 1

Share the best of you

SUNDAY 2

Prepare to get a good night's sleep

Own your own story:

- Say yes to your truth and your worthiness.
- Turn your wounds into wisdom.
- Allow your true self to be seen and heard.
- Say yes to joy irrespective of your personal challenges.
- Allow your natural creativity to flow.
- Let your inner music ring out.

Never ruin an apology with an excuse.
Kimberly Johnson

There is no agony like bearing an untold story inside of you.

Maya Angelou

Cocktail "Mai Tai"

4 cl White Rum
2 cl Dark Rum
15 cl Orange Cura
15 cl Orgeat Syrup
1 cl Fresh Lime Juice

Banana bread

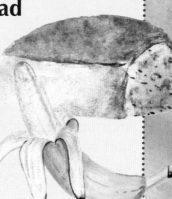

INGREDIENTS
450g overripe bananas
70g butter
175g granulated sugar
2 medium eggs, beaten
200g self-raising flour
½ tsp salt
½ tsp bicarbonate of soda
70g chopped walnuts

FOR THE ICING
25g butter
2tsp cocoa powder
175g icing sugar, sifted
Few drops vanilla extract
Extra chopped walnuts, to decorate (optional)

THE HOW-TO PART
Preheat the oven to 180ºC/350ºF/Gas Mark 4. Grease and line an 18cm (7in) round cake tin. Reserve half a banana for the icing and place the rest of the bananas in a mixing bowl. Mash until smooth, then set aside. In a large mixing bowl, beat together the butter and sugar until pale and fluffy. Gradually add the eggs and bananas, and beat until smooth. Stir in the flour, salt and bicarbonate of soda and mix thoroughly. Quickly mix in the walnuts, then pour into the baking tin. Bake in the oven for 60-75 mins or until a skewer inserted into the middle comes out clean. Turn out the banana cake and leave to cool on a wire rack. To make the icing, place the butter and cocoa powder in a small saucepan. Heat until melted. Mash the reserved banana until very smooth. Add the melted butter mixture to the mashed banana and beat well, then add the icing sugar and vanilla extract. Beat thoroughly until very smooth. Use to ice the top of the banana cake once it has cooled. Decorate with chopped walnuts if you wish.

I could not, at any age, be content to take my place by the fireside and simply look on. Life was meant to be lived. Curiosity must be kept alive. One must never, for whatever reason, turn his back on life.

Eleanor Roosevelt

Life is not measured by the number of breaths we take, but by the moments that take our breath away.

Maya Angelou

June

Love is friendship that has caught fire.
It is quiet understanding, mutual confidence,
sharing and forgiving. It is loyalty through good
and bad times. It settles for less than perfection
and makes allowances for human weaknesses.

Ann Landers

MONDAY 3
Bank holiday

Be great in small things

TUESDAY 4

Break a bad habit

WEDNESDAY 5

Face the reality of the world with courage

THURSDAY 6

A great structure requires a strong foundation of integrity

When a woman becomes her own best friend, life is easier.

FRIDAY 7

Have a worry free day

SATURDAY 8

Connect with your bigger why

SUNDAY 9

You can do it

After all those years as a woman hearing 'not thin enough' 'not pretty enough' 'not smart enough' 'not this enough' 'not that enough' I woke up one morning and realised who was doing the talking. So I stopped listening to her! 'I am enough'.

There is a special place in hell for women who don't help other women.

Madeline Albright

My imaginary friend thinks she has problems.

MONDAY **10**

Lighten up

TUESDAY **11**

Be your own best friend

WEDNESDAY **12**

Avoid self pity

THURSDAY **13**

Reach out to others – take the first step

FRIDAY **14**

Assess your strengths accurately

It's ok not to know

It's ok to be uncomfortable in the space between what is gone and what is coming.

It's ok to experience all of the emotions that come with being on the edge.

It's ok to take the time to slow down, get quiet, and sift through the thoughts, emotions and feelings that arise.

It's ok to feel strong and courageous, excited and fearful, vulnerable and unsure - all at the same time.

It's ok to be both the leader and the follower.

It's ok to be the teacher and the student.

THINK POSITIVE

It's ok to feel both anticipation that your dreams are on their way and the fears that they may not arrive.

TALK POSITIVE

It's ok to take time to quiet your mind so you can hear the wisdom of your soul.

It's ok to be exactly who you are—your powerful, authentic, loving and vulnerable self.

It's ok to let your light shine and let your heart lead.

It's ok to trust that you are in the perfect place, right where you are, in this very moment.

It's ok to be YOU, here now!

It's ok not to know the next step.

It's ok to ask for directions.

FEEL POSITIVE

June

You take your life in your own hands, and what happens? A terrible thing, no one to blame.

Erica Jong

SATURDAY **15**

Be true to your own heart

SUNDAY **16**
Father's Day

Remember you always have a choice

I'd much rather be a woman than a man. Women can cry, they can wear cute clothes and they're the first to be rescued off sinking ships.

Gilda Radner

When women go wrong, men go right after them.

Mae West

Men marry women in the hope that they will never change. Women marry men in the hope that they will change. Invariably both are disappointed.

Albert Einstein

Your mind needs exercise just as much as your body does, that's why I think of jogging every day.

MONDAY **17**

Say nice things

TUESDAY **18**

Learn to listen generously

WEDNESDAY **19**

Stand up for what you believe in

THURSDAY **20**

Decide to have a great day

I've come to believe that each of us has a personal calling that's as unique as a fingerprint – and that the best way to succeed is to discover what you love and then find a way to offer it to others in the form of service, working hard, and also allowing the energy of the universe to lead you.

Oprah Winfrey

Of course I talk to myself — sometimes I need expert advice.

FRIDAY **21**

Surprise someone with a spontaneous treat

SATURDAY **22**

Slow down

SUNDAY **23**

Develop a forgiving attitude

**Hold fast to dreams
For if dreams die
Life is a broken-winged bird
That cannot fly.
Hold fast to dreams
For when dreams go
Life is a barren field
Frozen with snow.**
Langston Hughes

What you get by achieving your goals is not as important as what you become by achieving your goals.
Zig Ziglar

June

COOL TIP
Chill white wine with frozen grapes so you're not watering it down.

MONDAY 24

Explore the limits of your comfort zone

TUESDAY 25

Put on your own oxygen mask first

WEDNESDAY 26

Let go of what you cannot control

THURSDAY 27

Be generous with hugs and handshakes

How to raise happy, healthy, confident children:

Be a happy, healthy, confident parent.
Enjoy the time you spend with them.
Speak words of encouragement.
Remind them they are unique and valuable.
Encourage their friendships.
Accept their best effort as their best effort.
Don't compare them to others.
Encourage them to join in activities.
Answer their questions honestly.
Listen openly to their concerns.
Love them unconditionally.
Don't be afraid to let them make their own mistakes.
Trust yourself – you're already doing a great job!

FRIDAY 28

Deal with unfinished business

SATURDAY 29

Let go of negativity

SUNDAY 30

Change your mind and change your life

BUCKET LIST

for
July

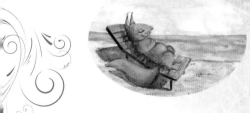

I made a huge to do list for today. I just can't figure out who's going to do it.

_____
_____
_____
_____
_____
_____
_____
_____
_____
_____
_____
_____

No one ever died from sleeping in an unmade bed.
Erma Bombek

MONDAY **1**

Count your blessings

July

Don't force your children into your ways, for they are born for a different time.

Plato

As we grow old, the beauty steals inward.

TUESDAY 2

Don't be limited by your own limited thinking

WEDNESDAY 3

Let yourself daydream

THURSDAY 4

A good book is a great companion

FRIDAY 5

Keep your own house in order

HEARTPRINTS

Wherever our hands touch, we leave fingerprints;
on walls, on furniture, on doorknobs,
dishes, books. There's no escape.
As we touch, we leave our mark.
Wherever I go today, let me leave
heart-prints. Heart-prints of compassion,
of understanding and love; heart-prints
of kindness and genuine concern.
May my heart touch a lonely neighbour,
a runaway daughter, an anxious mother, or
perhaps an aged grandfather.
Let me go out today to leave heart-prints.
And if someone should say "I felt your touch"
may they also sense the love that
is deep within my heart.

LOVE

SATURDAY 6

Look at your situation from another's perspective

SUNDAY 7

Let others lead and be content with the light they shine

July

We're in a freefall into the future. We don't know where we are going. Things are changing so fast, and always when you are going through a long tunnel, anxiety comes along. All you have to do, to transform your hell into a paradise, is to turn your fall into a voluntary act. It's a very interesting shift of perspective, and that's all it is. With joyful participation in the sorrows, everything changes!

Joseph Campbell

MONDAY 8

Be open to the contribution of others

TUESDAY 9

Take time to reflect and look inward for answers

WEDNESDAY 10

Allow yourself to be supported

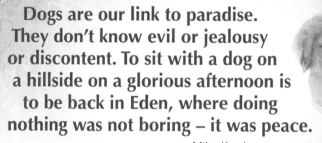

Dogs are our link to paradise.
They don't know evil or jealousy
or discontent. To sit with a dog on
a hillside on a glorious afternoon is
to be back in Eden, where doing
nothing was not boring – it was peace.

Milan Kundera

THURSDAY **11**

End the struggle and dance with life

FRIDAY **12**

Respect the opinions of others

SATURDAY **13**

Prepare for the next step

SUNDAY **14**

Seek advice and feedback from trusted sources

July

Don't be discouraged if your children reject your advice. Years later they will offer it to their own offspring.

Oscar Wilde

MONDAY 15

Build bridges

TUESDAY 16

Seize the opportunity

WEDNESDAY 17

Be open to entirely new possibilities

THURSDAY 18

Help others to help themselves

We must believe that we are gifted for something, and that this thing, at whatever cost, must be attained.

Marie Curie

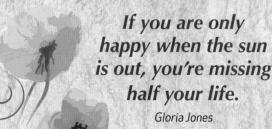

If you are only happy when the sun is out, you're missing half your life.

Gloria Jones

Success is steady progress toward one's personal goals.

Jim Rohn

FRIDAY **19**

Fill your mind with pleasant thoughts

SATURDAY **20**

No is a word that can stop a world

SUNDAY **21**

Compassion and kindness work wonders

A woman is sometimes fugitive, irrational, indeterminable, illogical and contradictory. A great deal of forbearance ought to be shown to her, and a good deal of prudence exercised with regard to her, for she may bring about innumerable evils without knowing it. Capable of all kinds of devotion, and all kinds of treason, monster incomprehensible, raised to the second power, she is at once the delight and the terror of man.
Henri Fredric Amiel

July

A dream is your creative vision for your life in the future. A goal is what you specifically intend to make happen. Dreams and goals should be just out of your present reach but not out of sight. Dreams and goals are coming attractions in your life.

MONDAY 22

Do what you know to be the right thing

There's a wise saying: make your hobby your source of income. Then there's no such thing as work, and there's no such thing as getting tired. That's been my own experience. I did just what I wanted to do. It takes a little courage at first, because who the hell wants you to do just what you want to do; they've all got lots of plans for you. But you can make it happen.

Joseph Campbell

TUESDAY 23

Forgive an old friend

> **Do not make your current partner pay for the crimes and misdemeanors of your previous partners.**
> *Amy Dickinson*

WEDNESDAY **24**

Every choice you make is a turn your life takes

THURSDAY **25**

All blame is a waste of time

FRIDAY **26**

Let go of any heavy baggage that is weighing you down

SATURDAY **27**

See the world through grateful eyes

SUNDAY **28**

The work will only get done in the doing of it

10 things to remember

1. The past cannot be changed but your view of the past can.
2. Opinions don't define reality, they simply express someone's view of their reality.
3. Everyones journey is different, concentrate on your own and remember it's a journey!
4. Judgements are a confession of your own character
5. Overthinking will lead to anxiety.
6. Happiness is found within when you serve without expecting return.
7. Positive thoughts lead to positive actions and positive results.
8. Smiles are contagious and kindness is free.
9. You only fail when you say you fail.
10. What goes around comes around.

GOOD IDEA!

Enlightenment isn't an over-abundance of thought. It's an optimal state of wisdom. It's the kind of thinking that dwells in wisdom and leads to love, acceptance, empathy, hope and art. It's the kind of wisdom that doesn't dwell in thinking, only to create, to experience, to act and to share. Enlightenment merely seeks the light to lighten the way for others.

Choc banana pudding

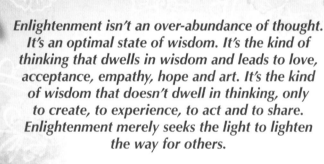

FROM MAMA RAE

INGREDIENTS
6 cups of bread
3 ripe bananas
2-2¼ cups milk
3 tablespoons flour
⅓ cup maple syrup
1 teaspoon vanilla
½ teaspoon cinnamon
1/¼ teaspoon nutmeg
1 cup choc chips

THE HOW-TO PART
Turn oven on to 180 degrees. Tear the bread into small pieces into a bowl. Whisk the milk, vanilla and flour, cinnamon and nutmeg. Add the maple syrup and stir. Pour over bread. Stir in mashed bananas and choc chips. Pour into a 9 x 5inch dish and bake for 30 minutes.

MAMA RAE'S INSIDE SECRETS
Omit the maple syrup and add six chopped dates.
Use two bananas and ½ cup dried apricots or peaches.
It is also yummy with ½ cup slivered almonds.

July

My favorite machine at the gym is the vending machine.

Caroline Rhea

MONDAY 29

Be at peace with who you are

TUESDAY 30

Take heart – miracles happen

WEDNESDAY 31

Everything can be resolved in a conversation

But we are living in a skeptical land, and, if I may use the phrase, a thought – tormented age; and sometimes I fear that this new generation, educated or hyper-educated as it is, will lack those qualities of humanity, of hospitality, of kindly humour which belonged to an older day.

James Joyce

BUCKET LIST
for
August

After all, Ginger Rogers did everything that Fred Astaire did. She just did it backwards and in high heels.

Ann Richards

The thing that women have yet to learn is nobody gives you power; You just take it.

Roseanne Barr

DESIDERATA

Go placidly amid the noise and haste, and remember what peace there may be in silence. As far as possible without surrender be on good terms with all persons. Speak your truth quietly and clearly, and listen to others, even the dull and ignorant; they too have their story.

Avoid loud and aggressive persons, they are vexations to the spirit. If you compare yourself with others, you may become vain and bitter; for always there will be greater and lesser persons than yourself. Enjoy your achievements as well as your plans. Keep interested in your own career, however humble; it is a real possession in the changing fortunes of time. Exercise caution in your business affairs; for the world is full of trickery. But let this not blind you to what virtue there is; many persons strive for high ideals; and everywhere life is full of heroism.

Be yourself. Especially, do not feign affection. Neither be cynical about love; for in the face of all aridity and disenchantment it is perennial as the grass. Take kindly the counsel of the years, gracefully surrendering the things of youth. Nurture strength of spirit to shield you in sudden misfortune. But do not distress yourself with imaginings. Many fears are born of fatigue and loneliness. Beyond a wholesome discipline, be gentle with yourself.

You are a child of the universe, no less than the trees and the stars; you have a right to be here. And whether or not it is clear to you, no doubt the universe is unfolding as it should. Therefore be at peace with God, whatever you conceive Him to be; and whatever your labours and aspirations, in the noisy confusion of life keep peace with your soul. With all its sham, drudgery and broken dreams, it is still a beautiful world. Be cheerful. Strive to be happy.

Max Ehrmann

August

How to be happy

More than 100 years ago, author Robert Louis Stevenson offered the following tips for maintaining a positive attitude. They still apply today.

1. Make up your mind to be happy. Learn to find pleasure in simple things.
2. Make the best of your circumstances. No one has everything and everyone has something of sorrow intermingled with gladness of life. The trick is to make the laughter outweigh the tears.
3. Don't take yourself too seriously. Don't think that somehow you should be protected from misfortune that befalls other people.
4. You can't please everybody. Don't let criticism worry you.
5. Don't let your neighbour set your standards. Set your own.
6. Do the things you enjoy but stay out of debt.
7. Never borrow trouble. Imaginary events are harder to bear than real ones.
8. Since hate poisons the soul, do not cherish jealousy, enmity or grudges. Avoid people who make you unhappy.
9. Have many interests. If you can't travel, read about new places.
10. Don't hold post mortems. Don't spend your time brooding over sorrows or mistakes. Don't be one who 'never gets over things'.
11. Do what you can for those less fortunate than yourself.
12. Keep busy at something. A busy person never has time to be unhappy.

Enjoy the little things

THURSDAY **1**

Never give up on your dreams

PRACTICAL TIPS FOR BALANCED SELF-CARE

Meditation for greater calm, clarity, and peace of mind.

Deep **breathing** practices to counteract daily oxygen depletion due to stress.

Daily **clear out** of challenging emotions like anger, resentment, guilt, and sadness.

Reconnect with your **deeper** positive motivations for greater fulfillment.

Calming **gratitude** practices to foster emotional peace and relaxation.

Yoga postures for **equanimity** and ongoing balance.

Build deeper **connections** through the expression of loving **kindness**.

Simplicity is the keynote of all true elegance.

Coco Chanel

FRIDAY **2**

Don't fear the future

SATURDAY **3**

Everything can change in the blink of an eye

SUNDAY **4**

Everyone deserves to be heard, so listen!

August

A woman with a voice is by definition a strong woman. But the search to find that voice can be remarkably difficult.

Melinda Gates

MONDAY 5
Bank holiday

Bask in sunlight

TUESDAY 6

Do not make yourself indispensable

WEDNESDAY 7

Every day is a new chance to start again

THURSDAY 8

Peace begins in your own heart

YOUNG AT HEART

Fairy tales can come true.
It can happen to you
If you're young at heart.
For it's hard, you will find
To be narrow of mind
If you're young at heart.
You can go to extremes
with impossible schemes.
You can laugh when your dreams
fall apart at the seams.
And life gets more exciting
with each passing day.
And love is either in your heart
or on it's way.
Don't you know that it's worth
Every treasure on earth
To be young at heart.
For as rich as you are
It's much better by far
To be young at heart.
And if you should survive
To a hundred and five
Look at all you'll derive
out of being alive.
And here is the best part,
you have a head start
If you are among the
very young at heart.
And if you should survive
to a hundred and five
Look at all you'll derive
out of being alive.
And here is the best part,
you have a head start
If you are among the
very young at heart.

Carolyn Leigh/Johnny Richards
(lyrics)

It's the plain women who know
about love; the beautiful women
are too busy being fascinating.

Katherine Hepburn

**Here's all you have to know about men and women:
women are crazy, men are stupid. And the main reason
women are crazy is that men are stupid.**

George Carlin

August

There is no such thing as an ugly woman.

Vincent Van Gogh

FRIDAY 9

Love yourself just the way you are

SATURDAY 10

Life created you to be fulfilled; go to work on that

Our life is so short that every time I see my children, I enjoy them as much as I can. Whenever I can, I enjoy my beloved, my family, my friends, my apprentices. But mainly I enjoy myself, because I am with myself all the time. Why should I spend my precious time with myself judging myself, rejecting myself, creating guilt and shame? Why should I push myself to be angry or jealous? If I don't feel good emotionally, I find out what is causing it and I fix it. Then I can recover my happiness and keep going with my story.

Miguel Angel Ruiz

SUNDAY 11

Avoid making comparisons

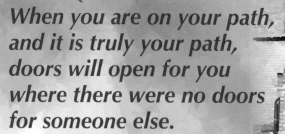

When you are on your path,
and it is truly your path,
doors will open for you
where there were no doors
for someone else.
Joseph Campbell

MONDAY 12

Don't gossip

TUESDAY 13

Tackle your problems head on

WEDNESDAY 14

Enjoy the journey

THURSDAY 15

Worry causes wrinkles

August

Don't let your mind bully your body into believing it must carry the burden of its worries.

Terri Guillemets

FRIDAY **16**

Hindsight is great but the best sight is insight

SATURDAY **17**

Life is an adventure – be adventurous

If you want your children to improve, let them overhear the nice things you say about them to others.

Simple spicy egg dish

FROM MAMA RAE

INGREDIENTS
12 hard-boiled eggs
1 onion
2 x 425gm cans diced tomatoes
2 teaspoons curry
1 teaspoon chilli powder
Salt and pepper

THE HOW-TO PART
Saute the onion in two tablespoons of water for 5 minutes on medium heat. Stir in the curry powder and add the tomatoes, stirring to mix everything. Add salt and pepper to taste. Serve with the boiled eggs cut in halves.

MAMA RAE'S INSIDE SECRETS
You can add almost anything to this recipe, celery, mushrooms, capsicums, peas, spinach. Add chopped herbs like parsley, coriander and basil. Instead of the curry try an Italian or Moroccan herb mix

SUNDAY **18**

Say yes to possibility

> **Before marriage, a man will lie awake thinking about something you said; after marriage, he'll fall asleep before you finish saying it.**
>
> *Helen Rowland*

MONDAY **19**

Don't doubt your capacity to cope

TUESDAY **20**

Acceptance is a sure key to contentment

WEDNESDAY **21**

Talk it over with someone you trust

The cave you fear to enter holds the treasure you seek. Fear of the unknown is our greatest fear. While caution is a useful instinct, we lose many opportunities and much of the adventure of life if we fail to support the curious explorer within us.

Joseph Campbell

At the end of the day, we can endure much more than we think we can.

Frida Kahlo

THURSDAY 22

Practice enthusiasm and watch your results improve miraculously

If tomorrow, women woke up and decided they really liked their bodies, just think how many industries would go out of business.

Gail Dines

Love yourself first and everything else falls into line. You really have to love yourself to get anything done in this world.

Lucille Ball

LOVE

FRIDAY 23

Believe in yourself

SATURDAY 24

Stay positive

SUNDAY 25

There is always a funny side

August

Summer
moved on

MONDAY 26

Measure your success by your level of happiness

TUESDAY 27

Attitude is everything

WEDNESDAY 28

Write down what you love about your life

THURSDAY 29

You are the author of your life story

I have learned over the years that when one's mind is made up, this diminishes fear; knowing what must be done does away with fear.

Rosa Parks

Perseverance overcomes almost everything

HOW TO PLAY A BIGGER GAME

- Discover your bigger why and let your bigger purpose drive your passion.
- Access your own deep inner knowing by being willing to go beyond whatever is stopping you.
- Resolve to heal any lingering self-doubt that keeps you small.
- Seek to root out and overcome those irksome internal issues and challenges that confront you when you need to step up.
- Find others who want to play the bigger game with you; create your dream team.
- Give up people-pleasing or perfectionist tendencies. A bigger game requires courage and a willingness to fail and learn as you go.
- Tap into the vast abundance of the universe and harness the miraculous energy that reflects your love and desire to contribute.
- Let the full power of your natural energies propel your team to win the bigger game you are playing.

SATURDAY **31**

Be prepared for surprises

Cocktail "Pisco Sour"

4.5cl Pisco
3cl Lemon Juice
2cl Simple Syrup
1 Egg White

BUCKET LIST
for
September

One is not born, but rather
becomes, a woman.

Simone de Beauvoir

fashion
log

september

WAITING...

I've wasted a lot of time in my life waiting for good things to happen, rather than acting to make them happen.

What I've learned?
Waiting suffocates power. Acting ignites it.
Waiting feeds anxiety. Acting relaxes it.
Waiting fuels boredom. Acting repels it.
Waiting galvanises fear. Acting subdues it.

Your life will not change any sooner while you wait around for something new. But it just may transform at warp speed once you take action to change it. If you see an opportunity, act, don't wait.

SUNDAY **1**

Focus on what you can influence

No person is your friend who demands your silence or denies your right to grow.
Alice Walker

Above all be the heroine of your life, not the victim.

Nora Ephron

MONDAY 2

Collaboration, not competition, is key

TUESDAY 3

Dare to live the life you want

WEDNESDAY 4

You are the master of your fate

THURSDAY 5

Be open to being vulnerable

Don't spent time looking for the meaning of life. Look for experiences of being alive that give your life meaning.

September

**Taking a shower is awesome,
it makes you feel nice and clean,
makes you sound like a great
singer, and helps
you make all of
life's best decisions.**

*I want to be like a sunflower;
so that even on the darkest
days I will stand tall and
find the sunlight.*

FRIDAY **6**

Notice the beauty that surrounds you

SATURDAY **7**

Stop procrastinating!

SUNDAY **8**

Your home is your sanctuary – beautify it

> Some of us think holding on makes us strong;
> but sometimes it is letting go.
>
> *Hermann Hesse*

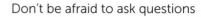

MONDAY **9**

Don't be afraid to ask questions

TUESDAY **10**

The way you think shapes what you see

WEDNESDAY **11**

Spend time with people who raise you up

THURSDAY **12**

Take a chance

FRIDAY **13**

Plan a Girly Getaway

September

HOW TO LIVE AN INSPIRED LIFE

Design a vision board inspired by your ideal life and place it where you can view it daily.

Visualise and blueprint your dreams in all areas of your ideal life, to the smallest detail.

Organise and prioritise the specific action steps to be taken to get from where you are towards your ideal life.

Dissolve, discard or delegate low priority distractions that blow you off course.

Work on the challenges of mastering a new future by recognising your old habits that draw you back.

Create a written **'Future Vision Charter'** to keep you on track with your goals and dreams.

Make a **commitment** to yourself to live your inspired life – one inspired by the **future you are creating** – every day of your present life.

SATURDAY **14**

Note to self –' Good job!'

SUNDAY **15**

Plan a retreat to spend time getting to know yourself

> *We all make the mistake of thinking that how we look makes us more worthy of love.*
>
> *Meryl Streep*

MONDAY 16

A positive attitude will open many doors

TUESDAY 17

When you don't know what to do, ask!

I changed my password everywhere to 'incorrect.' That way when I forget it, it always reminds me, 'Your password is incorrect.'

Too many of us are not living our dreams because we are living our fears.

Les Brown

♥ hope

WEDNESDAY 18

There are opportunities right where you are

In the sweetness of friendship let there be laughter, and sharing of pleasures. For in the dew of little things the heart finds its morning and is refreshed.

Khalil Gibran

Respect your uniqueness and drop comparison. Relax into your being.

Osho

THURSDAY **19**

Don't miss an opportunity to shine your light

FRIDAY **20**

Allow yourself to have fun

SATURDAY **21**

It's a changing world – keep up

SUNDAY **22**

Let your dreams unfold

September

You have to embrace getting older. Life is precious, and when you've lost a lot of people, you realise that each day is a gift.

Meryl Streep

MONDAY **23**

There is no magic in cynicism

TUESDAY **24**

Book a Day Spa

WEDNESDAY **25**

If not now, when?

Me and my bed are perfect for each other, but my alarm clock keeps trying to break us up.

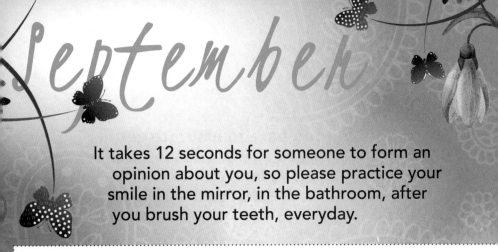

September

It takes 12 seconds for someone to form an opinion about you, so please practice your smile in the mirror, in the bathroom, after you brush your teeth, everyday.

THURSDAY **26**

Act decisively and accept the consequences

FRIDAY **27**

Who do you want to be when you grow up?

SATURDAY **28**

Fix the problem, not the blame

SUNDAY **29**

Explore new possibilities

If I had my child to raise all over again,
I'd build self esteem first, and the house later.
I'd finger paint more, and point the finger less.
I would do less correcting and more connecting.
I'd take my eyes off my watch, and watch with my eyes.
I'd take more hikes and fly more kites.
I'd stop playing serious, and seriously play.
I would run through more fields and gaze at more stars.
I'd do more hugging and less tugging.

Diane Loomans

MONDAY **30**

Never take anything or anyone for granted

Satisfaction often results in easing up on the gas pedal, a laurel patch on which to rest, drinking off your own success, caused by contentment. In this sense, happiness doesn't think; Happiness merely is. Marathon runners don't pay attention to the 26.2 miles. They pay attention to their breath. Their steps. The warmth of the sun. The roar of the crowd. The whoosh of the tailwind. Don't listen to people who tell you you can't – least of all yourself. I know you don't listen to yourself when you say that you "should," why change the rules and listen when you tell yourself you "should not?" Don't push away your dreams because you've "thought better of it." Don't parse through an endless array of worst case scenarios four or five moves ahead. Much of what we worry about never happens – what usually happens often does. Right your wrongs. Face your fears. Walk through open doors. You may not be satisfied with where you are at – but you'll be happy. You'll have discovered the secret to success in life without thinking too hard about it.

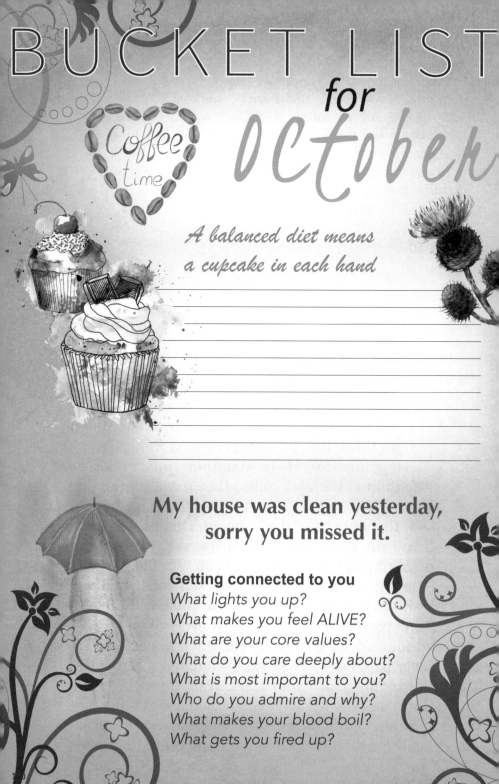

BUCKET LIST

for

October

Coffee time

*A balanced diet means
a cupcake in each hand*

_____
_____
_____
_____
_____
_____
_____
_____

My house was clean yesterday, sorry you missed it.

Getting connected to you
What lights you up?
What makes you feel ALIVE?
What are your core values?
What do you care deeply about?
What is most important to you?
Who do you admire and why?
What makes your blood boil?
What gets you fired up?

Each second we live is a new and unique moment of the universe, a moment that will never be again. And what do we teach our children? We teach them that two and two make four, and that Paris is the capital of France. When will we also teach them what they are? We should say to each of them: Do you know what you are? You are a marvel. You are unique. In all the years that have passed, there has never been another child like you. Your legs, your arms, your clever fingers, the way you move. You may become a Shakespeare, a Michelangelo, a Beethoven. You have the capacity for anything. Yes, you are a marvel. And when you grow up, can you then harm another who is, like you, a marvel? You must work, we must all work, to make the world worthy of its children.

Pablo Picasso

TUESDAY 1

Your beauty lies in your uniqueness

WEDNESDAY 2

Deliver on your promises

THURSDAY 3

Look for truth, beauty and goodness

october

Women are more powerful than they think.
A mother's warmth is the essence of motivation.
If we could liquefy the encouragement,
care and compassion we deliver
to our children it would
surely fill an expanse
greater than
the Pacific.

Louise Burfitt-Dons

FRIDAY **4**

Stay true to your values

SATURDAY **5**

Trust yourself to do what is right

SUNDAY **6**

Choose to hear

> Its amazing what you can get if you quietly,
> clearly and authoritatively demand it.
>
> *Meryl Streep*

MONDAY 7

Use your talents to the full

> *Ordinary riches can be stolen;
> real riches cannot. In your soul are
> infinitely precious things that
> cannot be taken from you.*
>
> *Oscar Wilde*

TUESDAY 8

Don't let your reasonable reasons keep you small

WEDNESDAY 9

Smile from the inside out

THURSDAY 10

The Joker will be the winner in the end

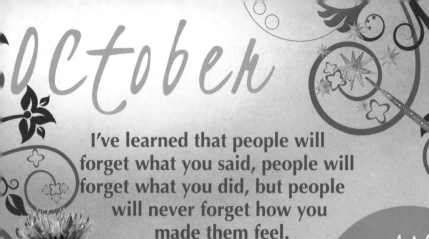

october

I've learned that people will forget what you said, people will forget what you did, but people will never forget how you made them feel.

Maya Angelou

Until women assume their rightful place on earth there will never be an end to wars, cruelty and oppression.

Fredrick Lenz

Obstacles are those frightful things we see when we take our eyes off our goal.

Henry Ford

FRIDAY 11

We each dance to the beat of our own drum

SATURDAY 12

Trust is the foundation of all great relationships

SUNDAY 13

Be responsible for your own choices

MONDAY **14**

If you speak kind words, you will hear kind echoes.

You never know what you have until you clean your closet.

TUESDAY **15**

If at first you don't succeed, try again

WEDNESDAY **16**

Be the bridge

THURSDAY **17**

Simplify your life

FRIDAY **18**

Look for the inner beauty in people

october

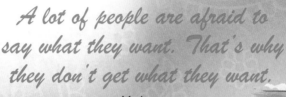

A lot of people are afraid to say what they want. That's why they don't get what they want.

Madonna

If you obey all the rules you miss all the fun.

Katherine Hepburn

We need women who are so strong they can be gentle, so educated they can be humble, so fierce they can be compassionate, so passionate they can be rational, and so disciplined they can be free.

Kavita Ramdas

SATURDAY 19

Take time for you

SUNDAY 20

Allow yourself a good cry

Taking joy in living is a woman's best cosmetic.

Rosalind Russell

> **You can take no credit for beauty at sixteen. But if you are beautiful at sixty, it will be your soul's own doing.**
>
> *Marie Stopes*

MONDAY 21

Let go of the past

TUESDAY 22

Expand your mind with new ideas

WEDNESDAY 23

Sometimes you just need to let go the need to be perfect

THURSDAY 24

Find a meaningful way to give back

FRIDAY 25

Embrace friendship

10 SIMPLE WAYS TO PUT WONDER IN YOUR LIFE

*Fill your moments with **wonderful** experiences.*
***Wonder** what new opportunity is about to appear.*
Be open to miracles.
*Love who you are, and **wonder** that you are so **wonderful**.*
***Wonder** beyond the predictable to wander towards the possible.*
*Accept that the world is all perfectly imperfect and **wonderful** just as it is.*
*Trust in the **wonderful** benefits of truth, beauty, goodness and happiness.*
*Don't **wonder** too much about the opinions and judgments of others.*
*Express gratitude for the **wonderful** opportunities that life presents.*
*Be willing to forgive – it is a **wonderful** source of peace.*

The more anger towards the past you carry in your heart, the less space you have for loving in the present.

SATURDAY 26

Go dancing

SUNDAY 27

You become like the people you associate with

MONDAY **28**
Bank holiday

Smile when you look in the mirror

TUESDAY **29**

Congratulate yourself on your achievements

WEDNESDAY **30**

Eat yourself healthy

THURSDAY **31**

What you discover for yourself is yours forever

Character cannot be developed in ease and quiet. Only through experience of trial and suffering can the soul be strengthened, ambition inspired and success achieved.

Helen Keller

BUCKET LIST
for
November

It may look like I'm doing nothing, but in my head I'm quite busy.

True freedom and the end of suffering is living in such a way as if you had completely chosen whatever you feel or experience at this moment. This inner alignment with, (and acceptance of) 'Now' is the end of suffering. Is suffering really necessary? Yes and no. If you had not suffered as you have, there would be no depth to you as a human being, no humility, no compassion. You would not be reading this now. Suffering cracks open the shell of the ego, and then comes a point, when it has served its purpose. Suffering is necessary until you realise it is unnecessary.

Eckhart Tolle

> **The worst sin toward our fellow creatures is not to hate them, but to be indifferent to them: that's the essence of inhumanity.**
> *George Bernard Shaw*

> *Hope springs eternal in the human breast.*
> Alexander Pope

Spaghetti bolognese

FOR THE BOLOGNESE SAUCE
2 medium onions, peeled and chopped
1tbsp olive oil
1 garlic clove, peeled and crushed
500g lean minced beef
90g mushrooms, sliced
1tsp dried oregano or mixed herbs
400g can tomatoes or chopped tomatoes
300ml hot beef stock
1tbsp tomato purée
1tbsp Worcestershire sauce
salt and ground black pepper

TO SERVE
350g spaghetti
Freshly grated Parmesan

THE HOW-TO PART
Fry onion and oil in a large pan for 3-4 mins. Add the garlic and mince and fry until both brown. Add the mushrooms and herbs, and cook for 2-3 minutes. Stir in tomatoes, beef stock, tomato purée, Worcestershire sauce and seasoning. Bring to the boil, then reduce the heat, cover and simmer, stirring occasionally, for 30 mins. Cook the spaghetti in a large pan of boiling, salted water. Drain well, and add a dash of olive oil, then stir in the meat sauce. Serve in hot bowls and sprinkle Parmesan cheese on top.

> *Well-behaved women seldom make history.*

> **Rest is not idleness, and to lie sometimes on the grass under the trees on a summer's day, listening to the murmur of water, or watching the clouds float across the blue sky, is by no means waste of time.**
> *John Lubbock*

FRIDAY **1**

Soak in a hot fragrant bath by candlelight

November

The most effective way to do it, is to do it.

SATURDAY **2**

Listen from another point of view

SUNDAY **3**

Nothing is more important than your own wellbeing

In today's rush we all think too much, do too much, want too much, have too much and forget about the joy of just being, doing and having enough. Patience is being at peace with the process of life.

Louise Hay

I do not fix my problems, I fix my thinking. Then my problems fix themselves.

You will succeed if you persevere; and you will find joy in overcoming obstacles.

Helen Keller

Your mind will give back to you exactly what you put into it.

James Joyce

dream on...

MONDAY 4

Life is to be enjoyed, not endured

TUESDAY 5

Keep focused on what you want to achieve

WEDNESDAY 6

Find the who that knows the how

THURSDAY 7

How you view the world is your choice

November

Though we travel the world over to find the beautiful, we must carry it within us or we find it not.

Ralph Waldo Emerson

FRIDAY 8

Let your love be seen in your smile

SATURDAY 9

Take small steps in the direction you want to go

SUNDAY 10

Listen to those who love

Stop looking outside for scraps of pleasure or fulfillment, for validation, security, or love – you have a treasure within that is infinitely greater than anything the world can offer.

Eckhart Tolle

The place between your comfort zone and your dream life is where your real life takes place.

MONDAY 11

If you want to make your parents happy, just be happy

TUESDAY 12

Plan a picnic in a local beauty spot

WEDNESDAY 13

Every problem has a solution

THURSDAY 14

What you do makes a difference

The simple part is, every thought you think, and every word you speak is creating your future. If you change your thinking you can change your life.

Louise Hay

November

FRIDAY **15**

Be willing to be brave

It's not vanity to feel you have a right to be beautiful. Women are conditioned to feel we're not good enough, that we must live up to someone else's standards. But my aim is to cherish myself as I am.

Elle Macpherson

SATURDAY **16**

Be enthusiastic

SUNDAY **17**

For peace of mind, give up being General Manager of the Universe

Security is mostly a superstition. It does not exist in nature, nor do the children of men as a whole experience it. Avoiding danger is no safer in the long run than outright exposure. Life is either a daring adventure, or nothing.

Helen Keller

MONDAY 18

Thinking is overrated

TUESDAY 19

In the end all that matters is that you loved

WEDNESDAY 20

Connect, collaborate, contribute

No matter how plain a woman may be, if truth and honesty are written across her face, she will be beautiful.

Eleanor Roosevelt

November

THURSDAY 21

Forgive everyone for everything every day

FRIDAY 22

Engage in meaningful conversation

SATURDAY 23

Don't wait; love your life now

SUNDAY 24

Let go of thoughts that disturb your peace of mind

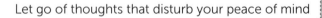

We could never learn to be brave and patient, if there were only joy in the world.

Helen Keller

MEDITATION HUG

To get the most out of the experience, Zen Master Thich Nhat Hanh advises doing the following:

1. Begin by recognising the other person.
Start by bowing toward the other person as a way of acknowledging their presence. Then bring yourself fully into the moment by taking three conscious breaths.

2. Go in for the hug (and keep your breathing in mind).
A quick pat on the back won't really do the trick here. Instead, hold the other person in your arms for three deep breaths. Hanh writes that the first breath should be devoted to you honoring your presence in the moment. The second should honor the other person, while the final breath should be focused on feeling happy and grateful for your togetherness.

3. End with gratitude.
After you release each other, finish the experience by bowing again to express thankfulness for the other person.

A dream collage is a picture of your goals. It is like your future photo album.
Bo Bennett

MONDAY **25**

All is well with the world

TUESDAY **26**

You are free to choose but you are not free from the consequences of your choice

November

WEDNESDAY 27

Choose to see the world through grateful eyes

THURSDAY 28

You belong, you are loved

FRIDAY 29

Invest money in experiences and reap the reward of great memories

SATURDAY 30

Learn how to prepare a new signature dish

You have been criticising yourself for years and it hasn't worked. Try approving of yourself and see what happens.

Louise Hay

CHRISTMAS SHOPPING LIST

1. Buy a 2020 Get Up and Go Diary for all my friends.

2. Buy a Get Up and Go Travel Journal and plan my next trip.

BUCKET LIST for December

Your success and happiness lies in you. Resolve to keep happy, and your joy and you shall form an invincible host against difficulties.

Helen Keller

Define success on your own terms, achieve it by your own (rules) strengths, and build a life you are proud to live.

FIVE STEPS TO MINDFULNESS

1. The five, five, five technique
If you find yourself feeling flustered or caught up in your thoughts and feelings, just stop and notice five things you can see, five things you can hear and five things you can feel or touch. It makes you aware of your surroundings.

2. Add this phrase
Pick any recurring thought that upsets you and replay it in your head with this phrase in front of it: "I'm having the thought that…" Then do it again adding the phrase "I'm noticing I'm having the thought that…" This technique puts some distance between you and your thoughts.

3. Thank your mind
We sometimes treat our mind like it is an angry teenager trying to get a reaction from us. Whatever it says, no matter how negative, nasty or provocative, try to hear it with a sense of detachment and say, "Thanks, mind!" And now for something completely different…

4. Breathe in, breathe out
Your breathing tells you that you are alive. In mindfulness you become interested in your breathing for its own sake. Observe the process for three minutes. You aren't trying to control how you feel, you're interested in observing your breath. You will discover how relaxed you feel in the process.

5. Put your foot in it
Push your feet hard into the floor, sit up tall with your back straight. Just take a deep breath in and out. Then relax your feet. The result? Your feet will feel lighter and you will feel better connected to the earth.

Dr Russ Harris

SUNDAY **1**

Invite friends over for a 'girls night in'

December

Laughing is one of the best exercises, it's like running inside your mind. You can do it almost anywhere and it's even better with a friend.

MONDAY **2**

Create a Vision Board of your future dreams realised

TUESDAY **3**

Commit to decluttering

WEDNESDAY **4**

Cross your bridges when you come to them

And above all, watch with glittering eyes the whole world around you because the greatest secrets are always hidden in the most unlikely places. Those who don't believe in magic will never find it.

Roald Dahl

What oxygen is to the lungs, such is hope to the meaning of life.

Emil Brunner

THURSDAY 5

Don't waste new tears on old grief

FRIDAY 6

Be genuinely interested in other people

SATURDAY 7

Take an after dinner stroll

SUNDAY 8

Let your spirit shine

Have you ever suddenly realised it's someone else's mood swing and you're just along for the ride?

Alex Bosworth

December

Chocolate brownies

INGREDIENTS
200g dark chocolate
100g unsalted butter, very soft
250g caster sugar
Four large free range eggs, beaten to mix
1tsp vanilla essence
60g plain flour
60g cocoa powder
15cm square brownie tin or greased/lined baking tin

THE HOW-TO PART
Heat the oven to 180C, gas 4. Break up the dark chocolate into a heatproof bowl and melt gently in a pan over simmering water. Remove the bowl from the heat and leave to cool. Put the butter and sugar into the bowl and beat until fluffy. Gradually beat in the eggs. Beat in the vanilla essence. Spoon the cooled melted chocolate onto the mixture then mix in thoroughly. Sift the flour and cocoa powder onto the mixture and gently stir in. When completely combined, spoon the mixture into the prepared tin and spread evenly. Bake in the heated oven for 20 mins until the chocolate brownies are firm to the touch but still a bit fudgy. The chocolate will continue to cook slightly for a few mins after coming out of the oven. Remove the tin from the oven and set on a wire cooling rack. Leave the chocolate brownies to cool completely before cutting into pieces. Store the brownies in an airtight container and eat within four days.

% chances of success

I won't: 0%
I can't: 10%
I don't know how: 20%
I wish I could: 30%
I want to: 40%
I think I might: 50%
I think I can: 60%
I think I will: 70%
I know I can: 80%
I know I will: 90%
I did: 100%

The soul always knows what to do to heal itself. The challenge is to quieten the mind.

Caroline Myss

MONDAY 9

Be grateful for the little things

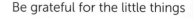

Give to the world exactly what you want to get from the world

Never cut a tree down in the wintertime. Never make a negative decision in the low time. Never make your most important decisions when you are in your worst moods. Wait. Be patient. The storm will pass. The spring will come.

Robert H Schuller

We are all works in progress, the authors of our own lives.

Caroline James

WEDNESDAY **11**

Take care not to stagnate in your comfort zone

THURSDAY **12**

Where you arrive is where it begins

December

The simplest way to be happy is to do good.

Helen Keller

Of life's two chief prizes, beauty and truth, I have found the first in a loving heart and the second in a laborer's hand.

Khalil Gibran

FRIDAY **13**

Quickly mend fences and move on

SATURDAY **14**

Be a tourist in your home town

Differences enrich families

There are two ways of spreading light. To be the candle, or the mirror that reflects it.

Edith Wharton

MONDAY **16**

Plan your work and work your plan

The most valuable possession you can own is an open heart. The most powerful weapon you can be is an instrument of peace.

Carlos Santana

TUESDAY **17**

Ultimately, things don't matter, people do

WEDNESDAY **18**

Don't complicate your life with fears and doubts

THURSDAY **19**

Never assume you know anything about anyone

December

FRIDAY 20

Relax, you're doing a great job

I do believe something magical can happen when you read a good book.
JK Rowling

Women never have got full credit for their bravery. They sacrifice everything to life.
Patrick Kavanagh

SATURDAY 21

Treat yourself to a 'be nice to me day'

SUNDAY 22

Give thanks for the best thing that happened today

I think the best role models for women are people who are fruitfully and confidently themselves, who bring light into the world.

Meryl Streep

MONDAY **23**

Think kindly of your parents, they are the source of your life

There are no makeovers in my books. The ugly duckling does not become a beautiful swan. She becomes a confident duck able to take charge of her own life and problems.

Maeve Binchy

Goals allow you to control the direction of change in your favour.

Brian Tracy

The girls who were unanimously considered beautiful often rested on their beauty alone. I felt I had to do things, to be intelligent and develop a personality in order to be seen as attractive. By the time I realised maybe I wasn't plain and might even possibly be pretty, I had already trained myself to be a little more interesting and informed.

Diane Von Furstenberg

December

TUESDAY 24

Take care of your body – it's the only place you live

Our deepest fear is not that we are inadequate. Our deepest fear is that we are powerful beyond measure. It is our light, not our darkness that most frightens us. We ask ourselves, 'Who am I to be brilliant, gorgeous, talented, fabulous?' Actually, who are you not to be? You are a child of God. Your playing small does not serve the world. There is nothing enlightened about shrinking so that other people won't feel insecure around you. We are all meant to shine, as children do. We were born to make manifest the glory of God that is within us. It's not just in some of us; it's in everyone. And as we let our own light shine, we unconsciously give other people permission to do the same. As we are liberated from our own fear, our presence automatically liberates others.

Marianne Williamson

Merry Christmas
Happy New Year

WEDNESDAY 25
Christmas Day

Free yourself from the constraints of negative thinking

THURSDAY 26

Spend meaningful time with your loved ones – turn off your smart phone!

In the name of friendship you should make sure your door is always open to listen. Don't feel you need to provide unsolicited possible solutions, answers or even ideas. Listening without judgment and offering assistance when asked should be enough. That's friendship's highest calling.

Amy Dickinson

I have found that when you are deeply troubled, there are things you get from the silent devoted companionship of a dog that you can get from no other source.

Doris Day

FRIDAY **27**

Everything is possible in committed dialogue

SATURDAY **28**

Don't just go through life, grow and glow through life

SUNDAY **29**

Show up to be seen; speak up to be heard

HAVE A HAPPY JAR

Find an empty jar and plan to fill it with "notes of good things that happen" this year. ❤ Then, this time next year, you can empty the jar and "see what awesome stuff happened" this year.

To acquire knowledge one must study.
To acquire wisdom, one must observe.

Marilyn vos Savant

December

MONDAY 30

Write a 'Birds Eye' version of your life story on one page

TUESDAY 31
New Year's Eve

Your past has got you here. Now what?

SLOW DANCE

Have you ever watched kids on a merry-go-round?
Or listened to the rain slapping the ground?
Ever followed a butterfly's erratic flight?
Or gazed at the sun into the fading night?
You better slow down
Don't dance so fast.
Time is short.
The music won't last.
Do you run through each day on the fly?
When you ask: How are you? do you hear the reply?
When the day is done, do you lie in your bed
With the next hundred chores running through your head?
You'd better slow down.
Don't dance so fast.
Time is short.
The music won't last.
Ever told your child, we'll do it tomorrow?
And in your haste, not see his sorrow?
Ever lost touch, let a good friendship die
Cause you never had time to call and say, "Hi"?
You'd better slow down
Don't dance so fast.
Time is short.
The music won't last.
When you run so fast to get somewhere
You miss half the fun of getting there.
When you worry and hurry through the day,
It's like an unopened gift thrown away.
Life is not a race.
Do take it slower.
Hear the music
Before the song is over.

David L Weatherford

CALENDAR 2020

January

S	M	T	W	T	F	S
			1	2	3	4
5	6	7	8	9	10	11
12	13	14	15	16	17	18
19	20	21	22	23	24	25
26	27	28	29	30	31	

February

S	M	T	W	T	F	S
						1
2	3	4	5	6	7	8
9	10	11	12	13	14	15
16	17	18	19	20	21	22
23	24	25	26	27	28	29

March

S	M	T	W	T	F	S
1	2	3	4	5	6	7
8	9	10	11	12	13	14
15	16	17	18	19	20	21
22	23	24	25	26	27	28
29	30	31				

April

S	M	T	W	T	F	S
			1	2	3	4
5	6	7	8	9	10	11
12	13	14	15	16	17	18
19	20	21	22	23	24	25
26	27	28	29	30		

May

S	M	T	W	T	F	S
					1	2
3	4	5	6	7	8	9
10	11	12	13	14	15	16
17	18	19	20	21	22	23
24	25	26	27	28	29	30
31						

June

S	M	T	W	T	F	S
	1	2	3	4	5	6
7	8	9	10	11	12	13
14	15	16	17	18	19	20
21	22	23	24	25	26	27
28	29	30				

July

S	M	T	W	T	F	S
			1	2	3	4
5	6	7	8	9	10	11
12	13	14	15	16	17	18
19	20	21	22	23	24	25
26	27	28	29	30	31	

August

S	M	T	W	T	F	S
						1
2	3	4	5	6	7	8
9	10	11	12	13	14	15
16	17	18	19	20	21	22
23	24	25	26	27	28	29
30	31					

September

S	M	T	W	T	F	S
		1	2	3	4	5
6	7	8	9	10	11	12
13	14	15	16	17	18	19
20	21	22	23	24	25	26
27	28	29	30			

October

S	M	T	W	T	F	S
				1	2	3
4	5	6	7	8	9	10
11	12	13	14	15	16	17
18	19	20	21	22	23	24
25	26	27	28	29	30	31

November

S	M	T	W	T	F	S
1	2	3	4	5	6	7
8	9	10	11	12	13	14
15	16	17	18	19	20	21
22	23	24	25	26	27	28
29	30					

December

S	M	T	W	T	F	S
		1	2	3	4	5
6	7	8	9	10	11	12
13	14	15	16	17	18	19
20	21	22	23	24	25	26
27	28	29	30	31		

NOTES

FOR MORE COPIES VISIT OUR WEBSITE
www.getupandgodiary.com
OR CONTACT US ON
info@getupandgodiary.com
Postal address: **Get Up and Go Publications Ltd, Camboline, Hazelwood, Sligo, Ireland F91 NP04.**

DIRECT ORDER FORM (please complete by ticking boxes)

PLEASE SEND ME:

The Irish Get Up and Go Diary **2019** ☐ **2020** ☐ €10/£9 — Quantity ☐

The Irish Get Up and Go Diary (case bound) **2019** ☐ **2020** ☐ €15/£13 — Quantity ☐

Get Up and Go Diary for Busy Women **2019** ☐ **2020** ☐ €10/£9 — Quantity ☐

Get Up and Go Diary for Busy Women (case bound) **2019** ☐ **2020** ☐ €15/£13 — Quantity ☐

Get Up and Go Diary **2019** ☐ **2020** ☐ €10/£9 — Quantity ☐

Get Up and Go Diary for Girls **2019** ☐ **2020** ☐ €10/£9 — Quantity ☐

Get Up and Go Diary for Boys **2019** ☐ **2020** ☐ €10/£9 — Quantity ☐

Get Up and Go Daily Planner for Busy Women **2019** ☐ **2020** ☐ €29.95/£27.95 — Quantity ☐

Get Up and Go Gratitude Journal **2019** ☐ **2020** ☐ €15/£13 — Quantity ☐

Get Up and Go Wallplanner **2019** ☐ **2020** ☐ €5/£4.50 — Quantity ☐

Get Up and Go Travel Journal ☐ €12/£10.50 — Quantity ☐

Get Up and Go Genius Journal ☐ €15/£13 — Quantity ☐

Get Up and Go Student Journal (homework journal) ☐ €14/£12 — Quantity ☐

Get Up and Go Heroes (all proceeds to charity) ☐ €10/£9 — Quantity ☐

The Confidence to Succeed (by Donna Kennedy) ☐ €12.50/£10 — Quantity ☐

P+P WITHIN IRELAND €2.50 PER COPY. P+P INTERNATIONAL/OVERSEAS €3.50 PER COPY. **Total number of copies** ☐

I enclose cheque/postal order for (total amount including P+P): _____

Name: _____

Address: _____

_____

Contact phone number: _____ Email: _____

For orders over eight items, please contact us on 086 1788631 / 071 9146717